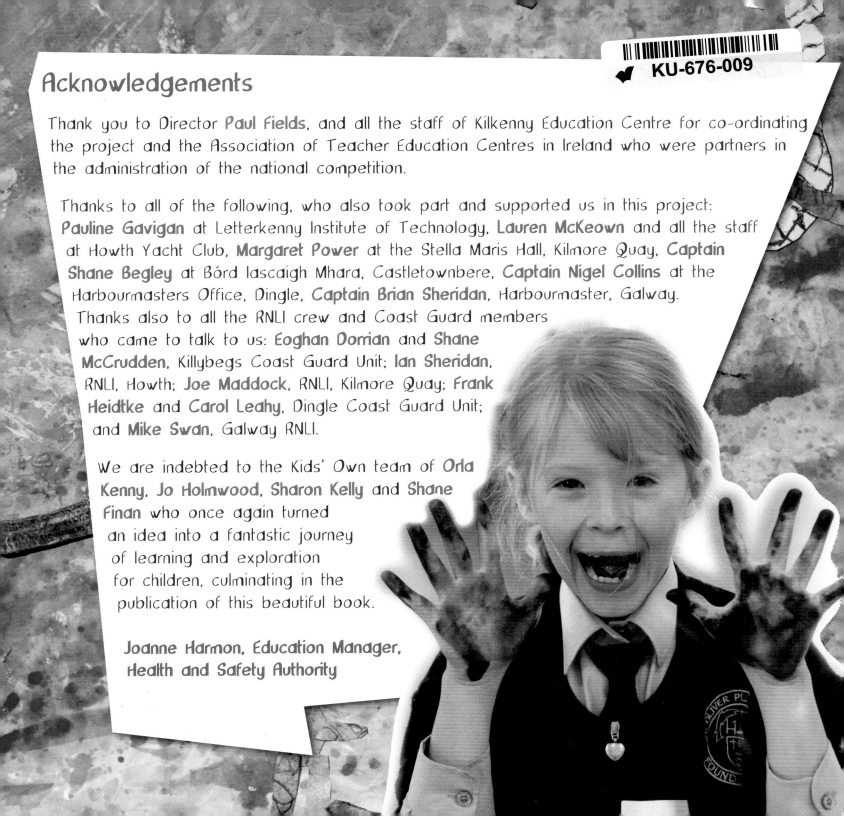

Acknowledgements

Thank you to Director **Paul Fields**, and all the staff of Kilkenny Education Centre for co-ordinating the project and the Association of Teacher Education Centres in Ireland who were partners in the administration of the national competition.

Thanks to all of the following, who also took part and supported us in this project: **Pauline Gavigan** at Letterkenny Institute of Technology, **Lauren McKeown** and all the staff at Howth Yacht Club, **Margaret Power** at the Stella Maris Hall, Kilmore Quay, **Captain Shane Begley** at Bórd Iascaigh Mhara, Castletownbere, **Captain Nigel Collins** at the Harbourmasters Office, Dingle, **Captain Brian Sheridan**, Harbourmaster, Galway. Thanks also to all the RNLI crew and Coast Guard members who came to talk to us: **Eoghan Dorrian** and **Shane McCrudden**, Killybegs Coast Guard Unit; **Ian Sheridan**, RNLI, Howth; **Joe Maddock**, RNLI, Kilmore Quay; **Frank Heidtke** and **Carol Leahy**, Dingle Coast Guard Unit; and **Mike Swan**, Galway RNLI.

We are indebted to the Kids' Own team of **Orla Kenny**, **Jo Holmwood**, **Sharon Kelly** and **Shane Finan** who once again turned an idea into a fantastic journey of learning and exploration for children, culminating in the publication of this beautiful book.

Joanne Harmon, Education Manager, Health and Safety Authority

I worked for 14 years on container ships and for 14 years teaching fishermen and I am Operations Manager for Bantry Inshore Search and Rescue. Fishing is the most dangerous occupation you can have. You're working on a platform that's moving, and you are surrounded by water. If you have a fire on-board, you have to sort that out yourself, and if you get a leak you have to sort that out too.

But it's very rewarding. If you ask any of the guys on the quay wall, they love it. The sea has a huge pull on you. When I was 12 years of age, I knew I wanted to go to sea.

Fishermen sustain injuries while they're working. They're lifting fish boxes and pots all the time. It's important to look after yourself when you're lifting things.

There are huge 'potholes' in the North Atlantic. It's the most unpredictable ocean in the world. Even 65,000-ton ships can get damaged. Hurricanes start in the West Indies and move in a northwesterly direction. When you look at the oceans, the Pacific and the Atlantic are the biggest. Two thousand miles of nothing but sea between Ireland and America. The prevailing winds in this part of the world are southwesterlies. There are big swell waves at sea. Once they reach the continental shelf, it can't go down anymore, so they can build up to huge waves hitting our shores.

Accidents don't happen, they are caused. It's a series of events. Once you get used to something you can get a bit complacent. Always treat the sea with respect.

Captain Shane Begley
Principal, National Fisheries
College of Ireland
Bord Iascaigh Mhara,
Castletownbere

"Fishing is the most dangerous occupation you can have."

Castletownbere (Southwest)

Shane told us what not to do when you get sick, like lean over the boat. And not to go on a float. If you get hypothermia you can get into this thing, it's like a sleeping bag.

You get cold shock if you jump into the water.

In Bantry sometimes when they're raising money for the lifeboat you get to go out, and I went on that.

Eve

You use a fishing rod and bait and weights.

Joseph

Gutting a fish…you fillet it and take out all the guts and make it into pieces.

Kieran

Sometimes you can't get the bones out but I'm learning how to get them out.

Every year for the Garnish festival we have a fishing competition. Gutting fish is one of the events in it. It's really good.

Shane

You shoot the net and tow along and hope for the best. You could be towing for nine hours sometimes if there is good fishing. We do two types of fishing. You'd tow for five or six hours trawling or you could tow for as long as you like.

Big massive nets – two boats tow it together. The net goes back like that. You go round in a big ring with the rope and you put out the net then and tow it. My uncle had his own boat and it sank. It just bowled over taking the fish in. She just went over. They're all fine. They all lived anyway.

They shot out the life raft and I suppose they just hopped into it.

We'd be going out with my uncle over the summer.

When I'm fourteen or fifteen I'll get my own boat – just a small one to go potting or whatever.

I help out. I'd be picking the bad ones out and throwing them back to the sea.

There's a poisonous fish with a big fin on its back and if that gets you in the eye you could probably go blind.

Owen

Those are the water gutters. If the water comes in over the deck it goes out the sides and you can close them up so that the water doesn't come in. That big wheel is the net drum. It's for hauling in the nets.

Those (pulleys) are things that pull in the rope, but they don't haul them up, they just keep them in line.

My dad has a boat for potting. Potting is like metal cages with rope around it to keep it from rusting and there's a net going in this way and this way on both sides. Lobsters and crabs go into those and they eat the bait and they can't get out and we haul up the pots and we get the fish. We bait them up again and shoot them out, and in bad weather we shoot them out a bit further.

That boat, once on the way in everyone was asleep and making dinner and they didn't watch out and the driver drove it into the rocks. They had to wait until high tide because it was low tide and they couldn't get her off the rocks. They had a big pump and they had to pump all the water and they only got to the sinker lift in time. There's a big crane above, a square with bars coming down with wheels and there's a big, very, very strong net, which pulls up the boat and will put her on a trailer.

My brother fishes on the Lauralina. When I went on it, they were going out to shoot the nets. There was a good few on the boat.

He's usually gone for about 3 days or maybe 5 days. Very rarely a week. Sometimes they go away 200 miles down. He likes it but it's very tiring and he's pretty tired when he comes back.

I do lining sometimes off the boat. You put the feather on the hooks and you have to trail it along. The second time I trailed it I got about 20 pollock and that's pretty handy for more bait.

Kieran

Grinders with discs, they can cut through anything. And hammers.

If you're down the engine room there's a big shaft going out to the bottom of the boat to the propeller and if you fall into the shaft you're dead.

Owen

All my uncles fish except for one. They all used to fish before. They're all my dad's boats – four of them. That's the smallest one. There's two others a good bit bigger than her now.

Rolling – You're 260 miles out to the sea. I'm going to be a fisherman.

Me and my dad always go to Gortahack – in Aran.

Owen

I'm going to go on a boat next week. We're going to a deserted island on a boat.

You can get hypothermia. Shane said not to wear adult life jackets if you're a child. You have to do this [swing your arm] so that someone will come.

I wouldn't really like to be out in the sea. You'd get seasick.

Paddy

"Grinders with discs, they can cut through anything"

One of our boats used to be a fishing boat and it's called 'Evil Bob'. Our friends gave it that name (it's from the Simpsons).

My dad is on the lifeboat. The 'inshore' lifeboat. He's only been called out about 3 times. I don't worry about him when he goes out. They don't go out very far. They only get called sometimes. One time was because of a big, big sailing boat that had capsized. It was the big lifeboat that rescued people.

They've got a medical kit and they've got this really sugary stuff for someone with low blood sugar level and they've got extra life jackets and they've got this thing that you throw out with a rope on it.

He went out the other day to some people who were stuck in Inishbeg and they only got half way out and they were sent back. I think someone had already got there.

On the boat they have this board that you put people on if they've got a bad back or something – a stretcher.

Sacha

My dad and my granddad, they used to work in the fish farm and now my dad works for the sand. He collects sand.

You have to tell someone — an adult before you go out swimming. Make sure you go down the ladder first and swim in the water before you jump off the pier, so you can get used to the water. If you jump off straight away, you're just going to get really cold and get a shock.

I've been seasick – you feel really dizzy and I have a really bad pain. I told my mum and she gave me a bottle of water. It helped a bit. And she told me to look straight ahead.

My uncle goes out fishing. He goes out for twelve hours. He had some exams last week and he passed them all. He usually goes straight to bed (when he comes home).

Emma

My dad, my granddad and my uncle fish. My granddad has a boat and my dad fishes on it, so the two of them fish together and my uncle has a boat as well. My grandad's boat is called Menhaden and my uncle's boat is called Eilean Croine.

I was helping bring the food on and making sure everything was right. I'm not a big fan of fishing. I get a bit seasick and I don't like the smell – it's fishy. Hard to describe it really.

They're always tired when they come home. It depends what they're fishing. Last time he was out it was January and they were out for a month. They had to go up to Denmark to paint the boat and then for the type of fish they were catching, they had to go around the Netherlands.

I miss them. Especially last year because that was the time of the storms. They were inland. They had to stop because it was too hard for them to fish in. I think it was Killybegs (where they stopped). I think it was maybe a week. Someone on the boat was walking down the stairs and his leg got caught on the step. He cut the heel and it was a very deep cut. They had to take him to the doctors to get it stitched up.

Zoe

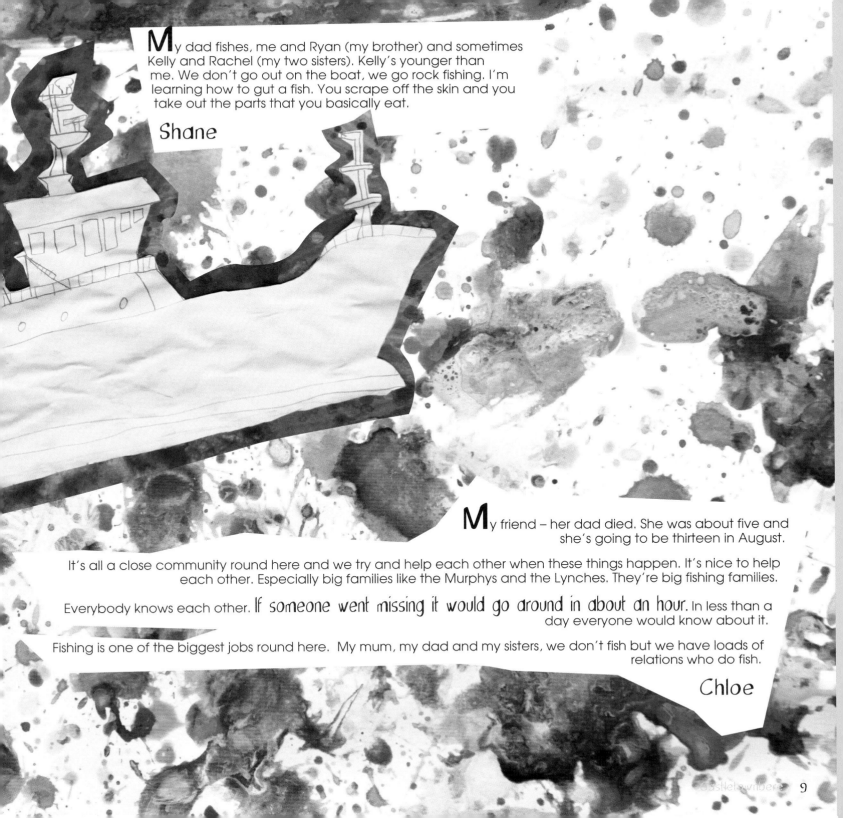

My dad fishes, me and Ryan (my brother) and sometimes Kelly and Rachel (my two sisters). Kelly's younger than me. We don't go out on the boat, we go rock fishing. I'm learning how to gut a fish. You scrape off the skin and you take out the parts that you basically eat.

Shane

My friend – her dad died. She was about five and she's going to be thirteen in August.

It's all a close community round here and we try and help each other when these things happen. It's nice to help each other. Especially big families like the Murphys and the Lynches. They're big fishing families.

Everybody knows each other. If someone went missing it would go around in about an hour. In less than a day everyone would know about it.

Fishing is one of the biggest jobs round here. My mum, my dad and my sisters, we don't fish but we have loads of relations who do fish.

Chloe

> "Being a fisherman has it's pros and cons. You get to eat fish but you could die."

That's how the lifeguard knows you're in danger. If the sea water gets into the triangle it wouldn't taste that nice. There is an orange thing and you get into it to keep warm.

You need to get used to the water before you jump in.

I've been on a ferry.

My uncle owns a speedboat and we're going out on it for my brother's birthday. My uncle got a baby, so the baby's not really allowed on the speedboat because someone could drop him into the water.

Katelyn

If you're in danger you wave your fist in the air...

You'd be squashed for 7 days (if you were in the life raft).

When I get my holidays, we're going fishing.

I'd like to catch fish but I don't want to eat them.

Shanice

The life raft was very squishy. (If you were in it at sea) it would be wet. I think my dad used to fish. He died when I was four. I found fishing rods in the shed. Being a fisherman has it's pros and cons. You get to eat fish but you could die.

Tim

My dad used to fish on the Oney Pádraig. It's a normal size. About 7 or 8 people work on it. He stopped fishing the beginning of last year. He got a job loading lorries.

When he was fishing, one day he was on the deck and he hit his eye off a metal thing so he couldn't fish for a few weeks.

There'd be a lot of people fishing so they'd know each other. Fellas who are fishing, most people would know who they were.

(If anything happened) you'd hear about it in less than a day.

There wouldn't be much work if they weren't fishing.

Paul

You have to breathe when you fall into the water. It's hard to breathe for about two minutes. The weather forecast is very important. It is very good but it can't always be relied on. Local knowledge is a huge thing.

It can be engine failure, it can be someone injured on board a ship, it can be a shipwreck...

The Breeches Buoy system would have been used for about 200 years. If there was a shipwreck we would search the shoreline and use the breeches buoy. The helicopter superseded that system.

Sometimes we could be out for three or four days looking for somebody. We would look for someone for up to 21 days. The fishermen are great for helping each other.

Frank Heidtke, Team Leader & Carol Leahy, Deputy Team Leader, Dingle Coast Guard Unit

Dingle
(West-Southwest)

Once I went down the Shannon on this boat called River Cottage and it was just me, my friend, my friend's mum and my sister, and it was quite cool because there was a sink and a table that turned into a bed.

I learned how to dive. You go quite deep. You have to get the right technique so you don't bang your head. You have to hold your breath. And you have to take a deep breath before you dive otherwise you might run out of air. We only went two or three metres. I know how to swim quite well.

Ruairc

I live in Dingle. I went fishing with my friend and her dog was on the boat and he kept jumping in and we had to keep getting him out. There was lots of mud and rushes in the river so we had to stay in the middle. We went out at ten in the morning and we came back at midnight and my mum was flashing her lights and waving her hands because she was out waiting for the boat. The fishing was fun except we didn't catch anything.

Juliette

My dad used to fish, but doesn't now. He used to do lobster and crab fishing and fish as well.

My mum did tell me once that my dad just dumped salmon in the sink – he put it through the window and it landed in the sink.

He misses going out on the boat but he doesn't miss getting the crabs out of the pots because once he wrenched his shoulder trying to pull the spider crab out. It was holding onto the side with its pincer and he hurt his shoulder.

Ellie

"He wrenched his shoulder trying to pull the spider crab out"

I'm from Ventry. It's about 2 miles from here. My dad used to fish when he was younger. He used to catch eel.

I have been out on a boat but I haven't been fishing.

You have to tell somebody where you're going. Just in case the weather turns bad.

Aisling

I live in Tralee. We went on a trip. We were going in a boat to dive. You have to have goggles. I couldn't lift the two bottles and so a man was lifting them. I saw lots of fishes. I was about 12 metres deep. It was rocky kind of and I saw some grass. Like seaweed. It's a bit dangerous. Something could be hiding. The bottles have air for breathing. You have to breathe through your mouth and not through your nose. I was feeding the fishes with bread. I think my mum saw a turtle. I can swim perfectly underwater.

Adrian

I live in Rylane. I was on a boat that went very low down and then high up, like a steamboat. But it wasn't doing steam. I saw Fungy the dolphin. My mum and dad were with me.

Aoife

I'm from Ventry. My grandfather and my uncle fish. It's their job. They go out in small rowing boats. They don't go out that often.

Clara

I live in Ventry. I did Splash and Dash camp for the summer last year. You go kayaking and you go out on a doughnut on the waves. It's a thing you sit in.

We went snorkling as well and we went out on a sailboat and Fungy came right up.

I did a safety course out in Ventry. You start with safety 1 up to safety 6, which is the lifeguard. I'd like to be a lifeguard – you get to be out on the water.

There's not much fishing in Ventry. They might go fishing on the pier and there'd be small boats going out.

Orla

I live in Ardfert, near Tralee. I've only been out for school tours. We go canoeing and stuff and we'd be on the trampolines and we'd be boogie boarding and stuff. I'm near three beaches and there's only one of them where people go fishing.

Caitlyn

I don't see any boats. There's trees and houses. I sketched a boat. It was a small one and Fungy. If you slipped you could fall in.

Aodhán

I live up in Ard na Gráinagh – just out the other side of Dingle.

My dad used to do quite a lot of fishing but we can't really fish anymore – only from the rocks because our boat got broken – it got smashed against the rocks. I think it was the wind might have drove it onto the rocks. It wasn't really repairable.

We used to go fishing and I think that once me and my mum caught an enormous fish and I think it was about that big (a foot). I think it might have been a salmon or maybe a bass.

He told me that he just went out around Dingle Bay and caught mackerel mostly and I particularly remember the time I was in it and we went out really far past the bay and it was about a 2-hour long trip. I felt as safe as I could feel really. You don't feel as safe as on land, but you still feel quite safe.

It was about last week, me and Ellie went swimming because we know each other very well and we went to Ventry Beach and the water was very cold and I got that thing that the coast guard was talking about, hypothermia, where you can't breathe and you're like...huh, huh, huh, huh....

Tomas

I live in County Kerry. I live close to the water. Fishermen should keep their life jackets on and make sure the lifeguard's watching. I've been on a ferry but not on any other boat. It would be fun to work on the water because you get to go fishing but if the weather went bad the sea would get rough and it might damage your ship.

Sarah

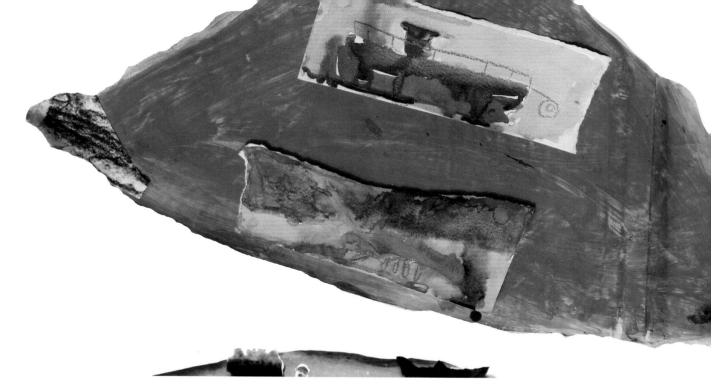

We had a storm in March and the signs used to be up by the dunes but now they're halfway out because the dunes were blown back because of the wind.

My dad would go fishing on the pier during the summer. The whole family would go fishing. We'd have to bring packed lunch because we go pier fishing and we also go shore fishing. We have to always bring a lunch and all the rods. About 3 or 4 rods. You have to go out into the water to cast on shore fishing but on pier fishing you just swing it out and normally you would catch a couple of plaice or bass from shore fishing but you would catch mackerel from pier fishing mostly.

The pier is kind of low so you wouldn't go up onto the steps to look over, because it is dangerous. If you look over you'd have to be either wearing a life jacket or something to keep you in so you wouldn't drown. And really you'd have to stay back and you wouldn't go and lean over a wall.

I think it'd be hard to work on a trawler. You'd have to go far out to catch fish and you'd be up against rough tides and big waves. Getting hit in the face by a wave would be fairly sore I'd say. You'd have to wear lifejackets all the time, definitely.

It's all slippery on the boat. You could fall off or go straight into a load of net. Or you could fall into something and all the stuff could fall onto you.

Reece

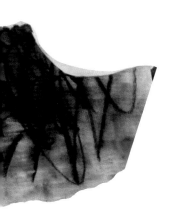

I live a little bit out of town.
You have a view of the sea when you look out the window. I think my dad used to fish a little bit but I don't know if he does it anymore. It's nice. It's nice to be on the water and hear all the sounds of the waves.

I like living by the sea because you can smell the ocean everyday and the sound is nice and it's very fresh and you get fresh fish in from the town. I wouldn't like it (living inland). It's nice being around the sea and once you're around it you can't really stay away from it because you're so used to it.

Ellen

I live in Ventry. We have a speedboat. It's quite fast. We go out looking for whales and dolphins and basking sharks. And we sometimes see sunfish. It's a huge flat fish with an eye on the side and it's got two fins, one on top and one on the bottom, and one time I was scared of it because it started jumping.

We have to practice man-overboard and we use the fenders.
They're like these bouys that you put on the side of the boat when you're coming into the harbour. When we come in close I have to get ready and when we come to the ladder I have to jump with the rope into the ladder. It's safe because we go really really close before I jump. There's no gap between the harbour and the fender.

The speedboat's not dangerous because it can't capsize. If someone falls out you have to shout "man over board" and then the driver stops the engine so that the propeller doesn't hurt anyone and then you start it again once you're sure nobody is in the way and then you turn around and go and get them.

Georgia

"You'd be up against rough tides and big waves."

I have 2 brothers who fish and my dad and me.

My dad has a boat it's a Helmetic 37. It's 12 feet wide and 37 feet long. And he has a dolphin boat. He does the Fungy trips as well.

We're cray fishing. You go out, you shoot your nets and you can come in and you leave them out for 10-20 days and you go back and you haul them back. There's a plotter in the boat and you mark them in where you shot them so you know where they are.

Blandies are weights on either end of the nets and there's ropes that come up to the top of the water so that's how you know.

There's this other type of fishing it's called gill netting. It's for pollock. With those you shoot the nets and you have to haul them after an hour or two because seals would eat the fish if you leave them too long.

It was very bad weather and on the boat the hatch was level with the deck and there was waves coming onto the deck and they went in and the boat sank. They were out for an hour. There was a boat out – it hadn't been out for a few years but it happened to be out and they saw them. They put a call out too. They had a radio.

I like going out fishing. I want to be a fisherman. It's kind of exciting because you don't always know if you're going to catch fish or not and when you do it's good.

Conor

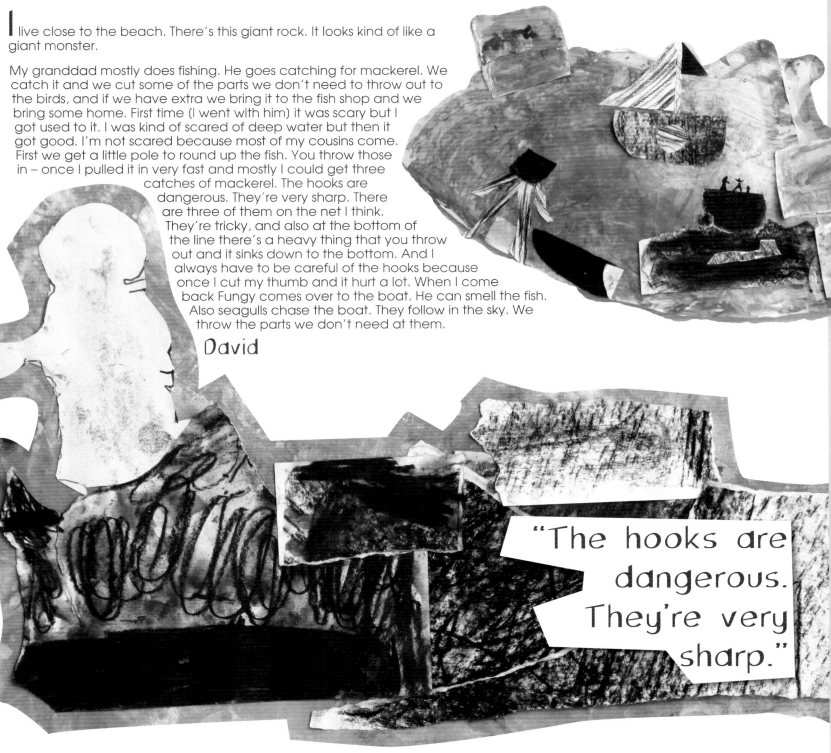

I live close to the beach. There's this giant rock. It looks kind of like a giant monster.

My granddad mostly does fishing. He goes catching for mackerel. We catch it and we cut some of the parts we don't need to throw out to the birds, and if we have extra we bring it to the fish shop and we bring some home. First time (I went with him) it was scary but I got used to it. I was kind of scared of deep water but then it got good. I'm not scared because most of my cousins come. First we get a little pole to round up the fish. You throw those in – once I pulled it in very fast and mostly I could get three catches of mackerel. The hooks are dangerous. They're very sharp. There are three of them on the net I think. They're tricky, and also at the bottom of the line there's a heavy thing that you throw out and it sinks down to the bottom. And I always have to be careful of the hooks because once I cut my thumb and it hurt a lot. When I come back Fungy comes over to the boat. He can smell the fish. Also seagulls chase the boat. They follow in the sky. We throw the parts we don't need at them.

David

"The hooks are dangerous. They're very sharp."

19

Mike Swan
Operations Manager,
Galway RNLI

Before I left school I had sailed around Ireland on a few occasions. On one occasion I was very lucky to get ashore on Skellig Rock (Great Skellig).

On the West Coast of Ireland, the waves work in a cycle where one in every eleven is bigger. We also have to take into consideration the tidal flows. The tide in a given day comes in and goes out twice. So we need to be very aware of the state of the tide when walking the shoreline.

How do boats move? Power driven vessels have an engine, which drives a propeller. Some of the services that the Lifeboat has to deal with have been where a rope or net has got caught in the propeller. The vessel can only drift in the water and waits for the Lifeboat to come and take them under tow back to port.

One of the services that I was on, it involved a local fisherman who went to sea in good weather conditions -force 4. He had fallen overboard at roughly 2pm and was located eleven hours later on a small island in Galway Bay. The weather conditions had turned very bad and at the time of the rescue it was blowing a force 11. The man was very lucky and made a full recovery. To this day he was thankful that he was wearing a Lifejacket when he fell in.

How would I describe the feeling experienced on a Lifeboat in rough weather? The closest feeling would be a roller-coaster ride, the only difference being that a roller-coaster ride would last five minutes where the Lifeboat experience could last for hours.

If you ever come across someone in difficulty in the water you should raise the alarm by calling 112 or 999 and ask for Marine Services.

Galway Bay
(West)

My dad fishes, and my brother, my granddad, me.

We do fishing with a line to catch mackerel, lobsters, pollock. We have a curragh. It's not really big.

It goes up at one end. It's made of wood. It fits five people, maybe more but it goes slower.

We wear life jackets. It comes down here – round your neck and ties around the waist.

I live on the West end of Inishbofin Island. It's not too small though. It's big enough. My dad used to sell it (the fish) but he doesn't do it anymore.

Niall

There was this guy in Limerick and there was this lake near where he lived and he was always messing. And he used to swim in the lake. He went down under the water because he could hold his breath and one time he never came up. He was down there for like, ten minutes and they went to look for him and they found him under the water and he wasn't alive. He shouldn't have been messing.

Aisling

Windy, the sea would be coming up on the roads that are close to the sea.

My uncle goes out with my cousin and they catch it to sell.

My dad wouldn't worry about the wind because he's well used to it, but someone who's starting, yes.

We live right beside a lake and there's small boats there but they're never used. And we live near a quay and it goes all around East Clare and people go round in a cruise on it.

Stephen

My mammy's friend worked in fishing but he died two years ago because he drowned in the sea. He was with his best friend. His phone fell in the water too.

Fishermen have metal boxes and there's bars on them and the fish go into them and they get trapped.

If there was little waves, some people might say 'oh they're little waves' but then a big wave could come along

You could slip on the deck.

Erica

My uncle owns a quarry but he shut down the quarry and he made a lake out of it. I go out on it whenever I can.

It's fun catching the fish.

Sam

It would be scary if you were out at sea and your boat tipped over and you didn't have anything to eat or anything.

Elizabeth

They have to have a life jacket and they have a radio to keep them company and to know when it's starting to rain or something. They have to have a fishing rod. Buckets for the fish. Or they use a basket (if there's lots of fish).

Sometimes my dad has to go deep because there's more fish. The further you go there's more fish. Sometimes I go. The life jacket keeps him safe and he's a really good swimmer.

Caolfhloinn

Do you often come out to the mainland from Inisbofin Island?

Stephen

3 or 4 times a month.

There's between 1 hundred and 2 hundred people.

There was a guy fishing on a rock one day and he fell into the sea and he was all cut on the rocks. He got out again and he came in.

Niall

There's a town near us and it's bordering Lough Derg. They have 5 piers and you can jump off, but you have to jump really far out because there are rocks and there was this girl and she cut her head and she died, I think.

Stephen

Fishermen would have a life buoy. Stephen

They have first aid. Sam

And a life raft. Aisling

Nets could get caught in the propeller. Stephen

If you were putting out a rope, your foot could get caught in the rope. That could happen easily if you didn't look where you were standing. Niall

On a big boat you might have a navigation system. Sam

On a small boat if you were sailing near a rocky area you could get caught on the rocks. Stephen

Fish have a 6 second memory. Sam

They put them into barrels of salt. Aisling

Surround them in ice. Stephen

They put ice under them and ice on top of them. Niall

They're pulling nets and ropes. Stephen

Carrying heavy fish. Aisling

People who work on the ocean do it because they enjoy it.

Aisling

On the island, you'd be outside more, fishing and farming. Most people would have boats.

Niall

I went on a ferry when I was a baby. There was cows on it and all.

The boats had ropes on the side of them and they have lots of boxes.

Roisín

Large boats have engines.

Nicole

I don't think the engines are safe because they might blow or a little hole might get in them.

Eoghan

They use nets. They're not safe because the net could get stuck in the engine.

Ksawery

I think it'd be dangerous. The fish could be heavy and they might pull you down. If you were very close to the sea and the wind blew you could fall in. Eoghan

Nets and ropes are dangerous. Ksawery

We saw a big crane to lift the boat into the water. We saw how the RNLI get dressed and the tools they wear. They wear helmets and they wear a suit.

Eoghan

They wear a suit to go in the water. Ksawery

One of the suits is kind of black and the other one is yellow and it's got the boots attached so you can get into them quickly. If the person was in the sea, they could drown.

Roisín

The fisherman was on the island at 2 o'clock and they rescued him at half past one in the morning. It was cold and it was raining and there was big waves. It was stormy. It'd be cold out at sea. It was very dark. He felt like he wanted to go home. You'd be lonely and you'd feel a bit sad and you'd be homesick.

Eoghan

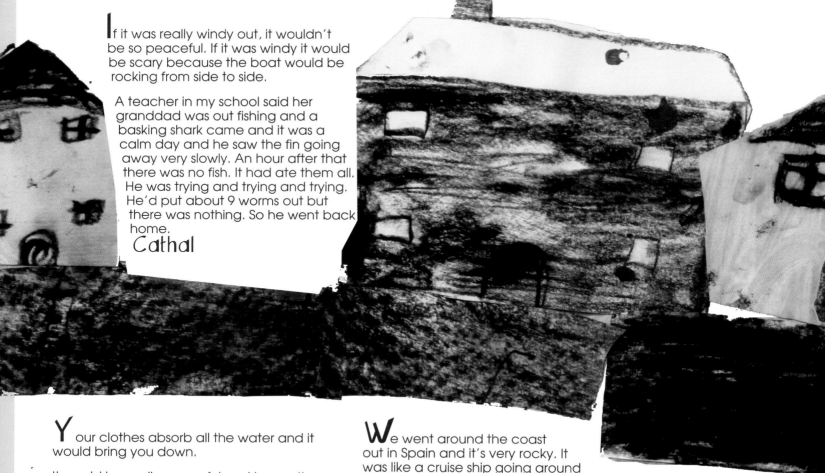

If it was really windy out, it wouldn't be so peaceful. If it was windy it would be scary because the boat would be rocking from side to side.

A teacher in my school said her granddad was out fishing and a basking shark came and it was a calm day and he saw the fin going away very slowly. An hour after that there was no fish. It had ate them all. He was trying and trying and trying. He'd put about 9 worms out but there was nothing. So he went back home.

Cathal

Your clothes absorb all the water and it would bring you down.

It would be really peaceful working on the sea.

There'd be a lot of responsibility (as a member of the rescue team), if you were the only person.

You have the big nets and you catch the fish.

There might be a hole in the ship. If it crashed or if a wave came it could weigh it down.

Enda

When the fishermen are going out to sea, they should put their speed limit low in case they go crashing. I went on holidays on a boat. It was a big boat.

You would be going to different countries to pick up stuff.

Eoghan

We went around the coast out in Spain and it's very rocky. It was like a cruise ship going around and it had a glass ground so you could look into the water. There was loads of fish and baby sharks swimming.

They had the life ring and they had loads of ropes and ladders in case anyone fell over and they could just swim up to the boat. And they had life jackets and we got to swim in the water. They had the anchor down and the boat had stopped.

Being a fisherman would be scary. Catching crabs and things, the traps could catch your fingers. Rods and hooks. If you're fishing like that (overarm) it could catch you.

Lauren

W hen it's stormy the ship might sink. You might be able to push a boat back over. It wouldn't be easy. If you had a life jacket on you might be fine. But if you let go you could fall down into the water. I'd get seasick – It feels kind of pukey.

Emily

O nce I went on holidays to Switzerland and I went on a ship and I got to see out on deck and it was cool. And I got to see the engine and it was moving. Some of the parts were red and kind of round. And some of them were going round and up and down. Dad went in with me to show it to me.

I thought it was really nice. It was like this really big space and there was people down there working it. I think it would be fun (to be one of those people) because you could clean it and watch it go round and round. It would be hard work too, because you'd have to make sure it was working okay and fix it if it was broken. It was warm. I think I would get tired (if I was doing their job) because you would stay there working the boat the whole day. Maybe if I didn't know that it was stopped working, the boat could sink.

Meave

T he eleventh wave is stronger than the other ten.

You should always have your strong hand holding on to something. I don't think all fishermen do that but they should do.

If there was strong waves then it would be fairly rocky but if they weren't strong waves then it would be alright.

There might be a bit of water on the deck. You couldn't really be a fisherman if you got seasick but there are tablets you can have.

Enda

"I think I would get tired if I was doing their job"

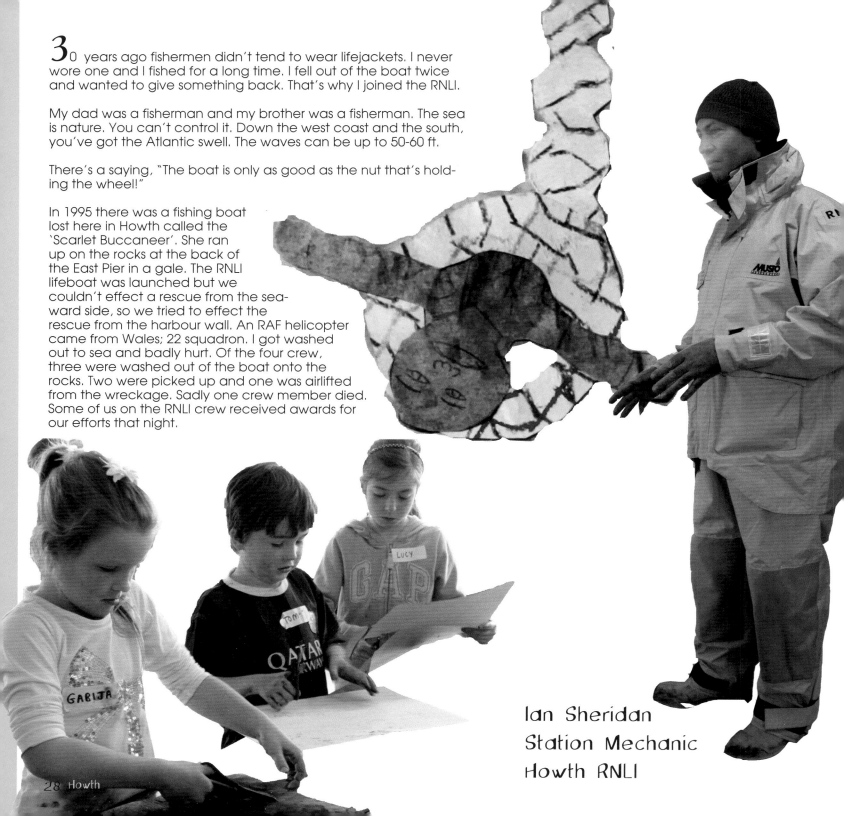

30 years ago fishermen didn't tend to wear lifejackets. I never wore one and I fished for a long time. I fell out of the boat twice and wanted to give something back. That's why I joined the RNLI.

My dad was a fisherman and my brother was a fisherman. The sea is nature. You can't control it. Down the west coast and the south, you've got the Atlantic swell. The waves can be up to 50-60 ft.

There's a saying, "The boat is only as good as the nut that's holding the wheel!"

In 1995 there was a fishing boat lost here in Howth called the 'Scarlet Buccaneer'. She ran up on the rocks at the back of the East Pier in a gale. The RNLI lifeboat was launched but we couldn't effect a rescue from the seaward side, so we tried to effect the rescue from the harbour wall. An RAF helicopter came from Wales; 22 squadron. I got washed out to sea and badly hurt. Of the four crew, three were washed out of the boat onto the rocks. Two were picked up and one was airlifted from the wreckage. Sadly one crew member died. Some of us on the RNLI crew received awards for our efforts that night.

Ian Sheridan
Station Mechanic
Howth RNLI

Some of the rules of ocean safety: Don't go to the sand bar or bank. My cousins own a kayak and when they come over to the beach we go kayaking. I haven't been out in the sea but in the rivers. Sometimes the currents push the kayak in different directions. Never pick up something that can throw it, because if the kayak capsizes normally you can get out but if you have a football or something it can catch your legs and you can't get out.

You have to be watchful for the tide. Say if you're swimming and you lose track of time and the tide is coming in, you could be far out enough for the currents to take you. The current is really strong.

Sean

I do kayaking. It's really fun. You must always wear a lifejacket. You learn how to hold your paddle and what you're to do if you capsize. You have to sit up straight and pull yourself out and swim to shore.

Jack Power

"He does go for six weeks and then he comes home for six weeks."

My uncle works in the lifeboat at Clogher Head in County Louth. He does go for six weeks and then he comes home for six weeks. As long as they're gone for, they come home for that long. He goes to loads of different places. He rescues and looks for people. He has people on the boat with him.

Alicia

If you go fishing in stormy weather you wouldn't be able to do what you're meant to do. You'd be tossing and turning. Working on the sea is dangerous because the sea is unpredictable. Rocks and cliffs. If you run aground on them you could get a leak and sink.

Ciaran

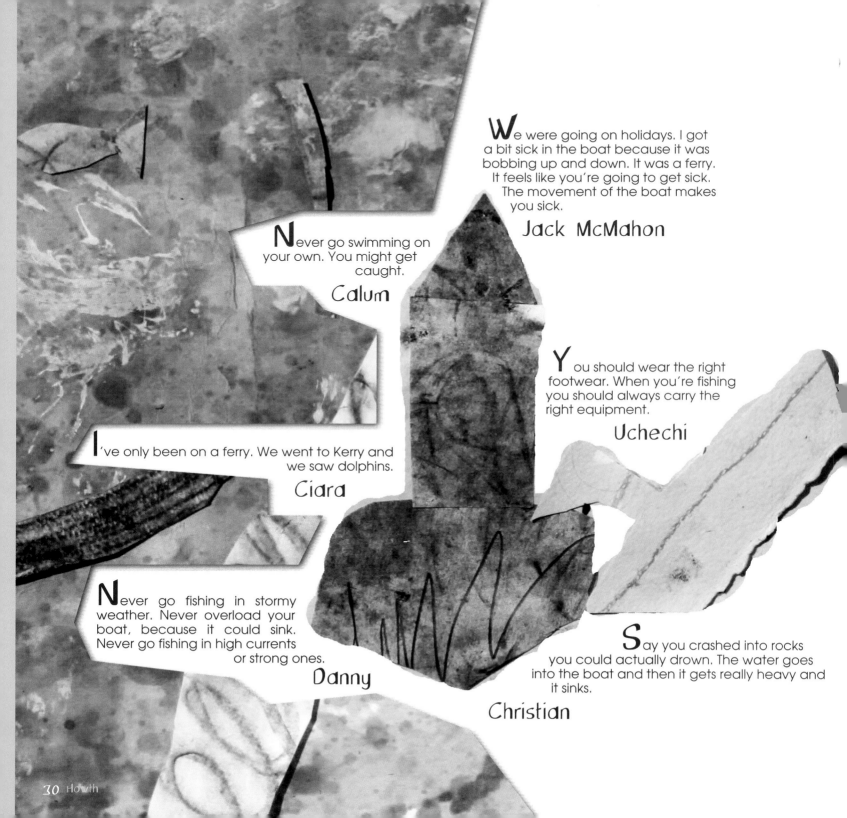

We were going on holidays. I got a bit sick in the boat because it was bobbing up and down. It was a ferry. It feels like you're going to get sick. The movement of the boat makes you sick.

Jack McMahon

Never go swimming on your own. You might get caught.

Calum

You should wear the right footwear. When you're fishing you should always carry the right equipment.

Uchechi

I've only been on a ferry. We went to Kerry and we saw dolphins.

Ciara

Never go fishing in stormy weather. Never overload your boat, because it could sink. Never go fishing in high currents or strong ones.

Danny

Say you crashed into rocks you could actually drown. The water goes into the boat and then it gets really heavy and it sinks.

Christian

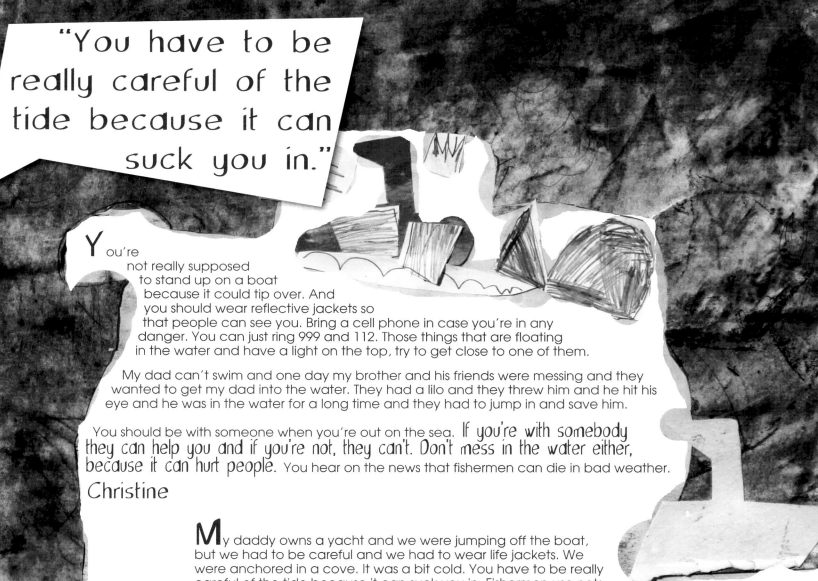

> "You have to be really careful of the tide because it can suck you in."

You're not really supposed to stand up on a boat because it could tip over. And you should wear reflective jackets so that people can see you. Bring a cell phone in case you're in any danger. You can just ring 999 and 112. Those things that are floating in the water and have a light on the top, try to get close to one of them.

My dad can't swim and one day my brother and his friends were messing and they wanted to get my dad into the water. They had a lilo and they threw him and he hit his eye and he was in the water for a long time and they had to jump in and save him.

You should be with someone when you're out on the sea. If you're with somebody they can help you and if you're not, they can't. Don't mess in the water either, because it can hurt people. You hear on the news that fishermen can die in bad weather.

Christine

My daddy owns a yacht and we were jumping off the boat, but we had to be careful and we had to wear life jackets. We were anchored in a cove. It was a bit cold. You have to be really careful of the tide because it can suck you in. Fishermen use nets and big winches for pulling up the nets and if you got caught in one of those you could get pulled up.

Lily

This year we visited Clogherhead seashore. We explored the rock pool. Tips to keep safe: Explore at low tide; stay in a group; wear old shoes; bring your bucket and spade; listen carefully; leave nothing behind except your footprint.

Orlaith

Use your common sense. Don't do anything stupid. Make sure your boat's in good condition. Make sure the engine's working properly. Make sure there's no holes.

Dearbhla

"We looked away for about 5 seconds."

If a boat gets lost, the lighthouse shines its light to bring it back. Fishermen should have boots.

Calum

"I was underneath the water. It was scary."

Make sure someone's watching you so that you don't go out of your depth. My friend was in the kids' pool on holidays. We looked away for about 5 seconds and when we looked back she was face down in the water. She had slipped or something but my dad jumped in and saved her. She was okay. She was coughing.

Ciaran

Make sure there's a lifeguard on the beach that you're going to. When I was one I was in Australia and I was playing in the sand and I nearly got washed away by a wave. My mum had to come and rescue me. We went to this island in Australia and there were these creatures and my dad and my uncle got cuts all over their arms.

Anna

Don't eat before you go swimming because you can get cramps and drown. Don't sit in anything that can float because it can get dragged away on the current.

I wouldn't like being a fisherman because I hate fish! If you fly fish, it's where you swing the rod back and forth and you throw it in. It doesn't sink, it bobs on the top and then you pull it back. My dad used to go fishing and the hook caught me in the leg. He nearly put me out. Fishermen have big buckets of bait, worms that you put on the hook.

David

Someone asked me if I wanted to go on this thing like a boat made out of rubber. There was a big wave coming and they said this is a good wave and when the wave came I was pulled into the shore and I was underneath the water. It was scary and when the wave went away I got out.

Poppy

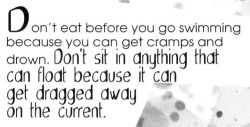

Daddy has a boat and I went on it. We had to wear a lifejacket. It was very rocky. Sailors and fishermen work on the sea. If they don't wear their lifejackets, they could drown. You would be rocking from side to side on a boat. It would be cold. Fishermen would find it hard to sleep at night.

Neena

If it was snowing, it would be freezing. And if it was raining you would have to work in the rain. It would be horrible and wet. If there was lightning you could get struck.

Lucy

The boat and the sea is their workplace. If you were out during the night and a storm suddenly came you could be tossed off the boat. If you were out on the sea and it started raining and you hadn't caught any fish you'd have to stay out there. If you were working at night and you fell asleep or something, you could drift out to sea. If you have your phone you could call someone. But if you didn't have a phone you couldn't.

Even if you think you're a good swimmer a giant wave might come and it could sweep you away. You have captains on ferries, if they're going across the Atlantic. I'd be really nervous because I wouldn't want to crash the ship because I'd be responsible for tons of lives.

Ava

The navy work on the sea. That's the sea part of the army. If you were a fisherman your life would be very uncertain because your income would be dependent on the amount of fish you catch and competing with other fishermen and so you'd have to spend a lot of hours trying to keep up. You'd get very tired and become very unsociable with people you know.

If you're older it would be harder to wear a life jacket because you've grown up without it, whereas our generation have grown up with all the warnings.

You'd be lonely and you'd be worried all the time because you wouldn't be able to spend time with your family.

Jenna

"The boat and the sea is their workplace."

It's a rescue helicopter, saving a boat. You need a helicopter if it's too dangerous to go on the sea.

Tom

If it was night, a wave could come and then the people who were on the boat might sink. It would be dangerous if you didn't have a life jacket and you fell off the boat.

Gabija

We have a 300 horsepower inflatable rib. Rocks can stop us getting close to a person by boat. We also carry out cliff rescues.

Always check the weather before going to sea as the weather can change very quickly. Alcohol should never be taken while at sea or near the water.

There is a course called PST (personal survival techniques), which every fisherman has to do before going to sea.

On marine maps the numbers indicate the water depth, along with other details, relative to water-based activities.

You should always wear a life jacket and always tell someone on shore where you plan to go on the boat and a time that you intend to return.

Eoghan Dorrian &
Shane McCrudden
Killybegs Coast
Guard Unit

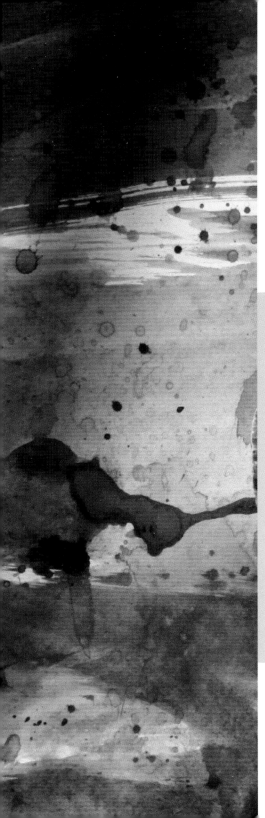

Killybegs
(Northwest)

Don't swim around boats because it might be dangerous. If they don't see you the ship could run over you. It would be sore. If you fell off a boat and there was no one there, you should cross your arms and legs and bring up your legs to your stomach to keep warm. One of my brothers gets magazines about boats and fishing. My family go fishing a lot. They have a very big boat. They have nets and fishing rods. You could get your finger caught on a hook.

Jennifer

You have to have special gear if you're going swimming. You need at least 4 or 5 flares and if you're going diving take an extra oxygen tank. My Dad's a diver. He went to Egypt in February for a diving trip. Your legs are always moving and your back's always full of oxygen to keep alive. It's somewhat dangerous. Some people lose their oxygen and you need to share it with another person. You have to share the same oxygen tank. It's wild hard to stay together. Your heart has to stay a certain degrees and your body temperature is the same. If it drops it's very dangerous.

My uncle Barry is a fisherman. He's staying for the summer. He was away a long time. Every month they leave at the start and come back two days before the end of the month. The boat is more their home than their real home.

All the water we drink has some bit of salt in it. It comes from the mountains into the river down to the sea, steams back up, turns into a raincloud and goes back up to the top of the mountain.

Shaun

"The boat is more their home than their real home."

Never set off one of those flares if you don't need it. If there's a life ring missing, you have to call and get it replaced.

There's freezers on boats. Working as a fisherman, you'd just have a fear that the boat might crash. I wouldn't like being a fisherman because I'd miss my family.

You could trip over nets on the deck. My dad works on a fishing boat and they work with crews. Crew is the people that work on the boat with you. You have rooms and you have a partner with you. There's a big massive freezer – it's really, really, really big. Always, always know the weather. It can change really quickly. The white thing would come up and it would be really dangerous. I like the sound of the waves.

Abi

My dad goes away with the fishermen and he would have to check on the boat. Most of the people who work on the boat live up on Greencastle, and the boat stays here. So he has to check on the boat, making sure that no one is on it, that it's tied up and he works on the engine, so if it's broke down, he fixes it. If the engine doesn't work it could break down wherever they're going.

Even on a big boat there could be a storm and all the waves would be crashing onto the deck and if you were on a smaller boat it would be even worse. On the big boats, they have to sleep in the little cubby things in the wall – there's just a hole to get into. It's like falling asleep in a rocking chair, moving the whole time.

My dad has a video of a killer whale flipping over. In America they call them, 'shamoos'. Most people are fishermen because they really like what they do. It's really peaceful out there.

Orla

I went off to see basking sharks in a boat. All you see is the top of their fin. This man, he went off fishing on our nearest pier. And then the boat started to sink. There were people there and they called the coast guard and they used the rope to pull him out.

Niamh

I went over to Scotland. My cousins have a kayak and they live beside a lake. My granddad brought us out fishing. He has a small fishing boat. It was a bit dangerous because my granddad was trying to fish with me and my sister on it, so the hook could have got one of us. If you catch a small fish, you have to put it back in, but if it's a big one you keep it.

Ciara

If you're in a group in the water and you're drowning you have to make a circle all together because if the helicopter comes they'll only see you if you're in a group. If you're diving be careful of rocks. You can freeze in the water. The seats on boats are like benches so that they don't move or fall over. If you're a fisherman you should always remember to keep lifejackets and flares and a radio on the boat.

A cruise ship is like a hotel on the sea. I don't think you can fish in water boats. They go too fast.

You get to see different types of fish and sharks and whales – sea life. If we never had the ocean and the sea where would we get our fish from?

Rimsha

I've been on a boat once – but it was just a little fishing boat, at my granny Rita's beach. Daddy just rowed the boat and we just sat there. We just stayed around the shore. I can't swim. There were a few people over the summer who drowned. I think it was on the beach. Trying to catch fish would be the hardest thing about being a fisherman.

Carla

39

"Being a fisherman is ten times worse than being a teacher."

Being a fisherman is a really dangerous job. It's ten times worse than being a teacher because you have ten times more chance of dying. You'd see lightning. Before you go fishing you should check and see what the weather is going to be like and if it's bad you shouldn't go out.

Jane

The waterbus is made of metal or steel or something. I almost got seasick. It feels kind of fuzzy in your throat. People get sick if they're not used to the water.

Aoife

If you want help, you call someone at the station. I think working at sea would be quite scary at first but it wouldn't be as scary if you were on it loads of times. It's the same as trying something new but then you get used to it. Without the sea we wouldn't have water to drink.

Trudie

It's stormy and you could die. You could crash into a rock or the boat could sink. I think it's scary when you're in the sea. I saw this movie called Jaws. Ireland's too cold for sharks but there are basking sharks. I like the shells, there are cool shells at the beach.

Penelope

The lifejackets can save somebody's life. Then they won't die. I was on a boat in Paris. It was boring. I don't think I'd like to work on a boat. It's a lot of work. You stay out for a long time when you're out fishing – a week or two weeks.

Shane

We were surfing and there was this girl and she surfed into the shore and the water was only about this deep and she broke her knee.

Andrea

I've been on the waterbus in Donegal. You can go out the back to see all the water. It's a big boat and it has flags on the top. I went to Rosnowlagh. I was there with my family. Sometimes you could see little seals hopping up on the stones.

Laoise

In the boat yard they make boats and they fix them. If there was a storm coming the sea would be very rough. The lifeguards have to keep everyone safe on the beach. What if the sea froze over? We'd have nothing to drink. All the fish would die.

Alina

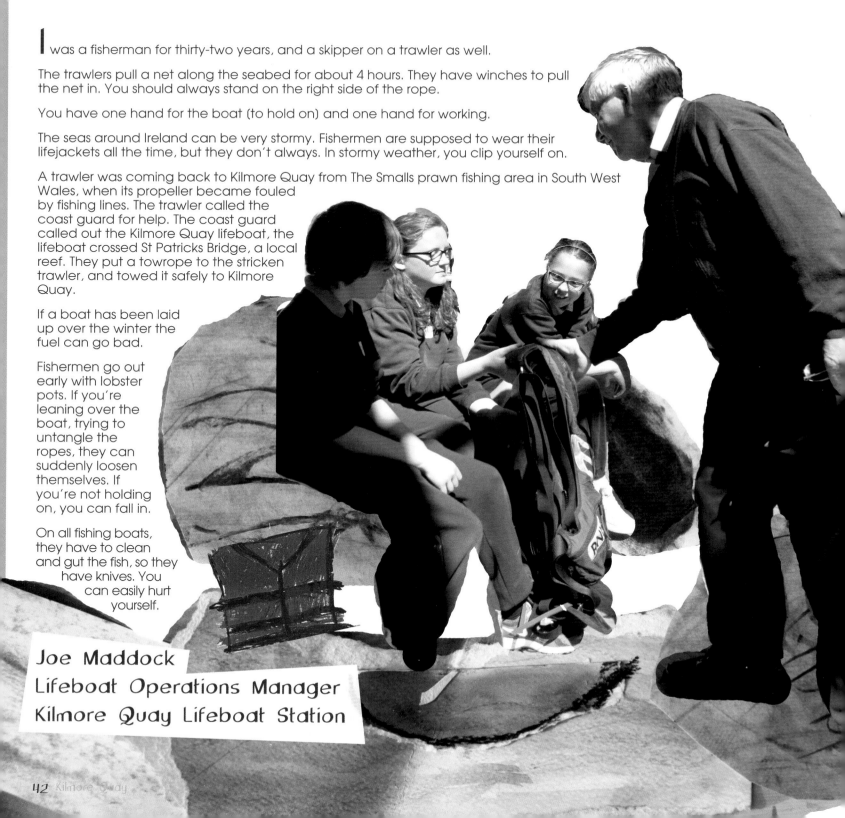

I was a fisherman for thirty-two years, and a skipper on a trawler as well.

The trawlers pull a net along the seabed for about 4 hours. They have winches to pull the net in. You should always stand on the right side of the rope.

You have one hand for the boat (to hold on) and one hand for working.

The seas around Ireland can be very stormy. Fishermen are supposed to wear their lifejackets all the time, but they don't always. In stormy weather, you clip yourself on.

A trawler was coming back to Kilmore Quay from The Smalls prawn fishing area in South West Wales, when its propeller became fouled by fishing lines. The trawler called the coast guard for help. The coast guard called out the Kilmore Quay lifeboat, the lifeboat crossed St Patricks Bridge, a local reef. They put a towrope to the stricken trawler, and towed it safely to Kilmore Quay.

If a boat has been laid up over the winter the fuel can go bad.

Fishermen go out early with lobster pots. If you're leaning over the boat, trying to untangle the ropes, they can suddenly loosen themselves. If you're not holding on, you can fall in.

On all fishing boats, they have to clean and gut the fish, so they have knives. You can easily hurt yourself.

Joe Maddock
Lifeboat Operations Manager
Kilmore Quay Lifeboat Station

Kilmore Quay
(Southeast)

Never turn your back to the sea – if you do you might fall in. My granddad had a fishing boat and it had lifejackets in it. My daddy works on a boat. It's a really big boat. He had nets and he caught crabs and all in them. You have to have a licence to drive a boat. Some fishermen get their fingers caught in stingers and crabs. Some boats tip over. If the whole boat tips over then everything falls out. If you're fishing you should know how to swim.

Hallie

My uncle Finny died on the sea. He was on the lifeboat and somebody called the lifeboat and it was a false alarm and he went into the water to look for the person and he drowned. They have a thing that tells you what the weather's going to be like. They check it just before. I've been on my brother Mel's boat. It was scary. I don't really like being on it. My brother started fishing and my other brothers tried it and they liked it. Eamonn and Finny they got caught on the boat when **the weather was really stormy and the water broke all the windows on the boat** and the water came in the front of the boat.

Claudia

I've been on the boat but not when it's on the sea. It's a big fishing boat with the beams. You have to be careful of where you're standing.

I was in the park and I saw all the boats going out to the island looking for the body of the man who fell in. It's really sad.

Kellie

"It was a false alarm. He went into the water and he drowned."

I wouldn't like to be a fisherman. It looks a little bit too hard and difficult. You have to get the boat set up before you go out and you might be tired. And then you might not feel like going out. The sail. You have to pull it with your hands and if it was a really big sail it could fall over and you'd have to get someone to get it fixed.

My brother's friend's dad is a diver. It's dangerous. They have to carry oxygen tanks on their backs. They could run out of oxygen. Something sharp could burst the oxygen. Then they'd drown. Unless they made it up in time. Then they'd be okay.

Daniel

My dad used to be a skipper and used to be a fisherman as well and he makes nets. I've seen loads of pictures and videos of him going out. When Joe said he used to be a skipper I thought of my dad. It's a hard job. You could get washed out to sea. It's hard to get fish, because you might get the wrong fish. You have to find out which place has the right fish. If you have a life jacket it's safe but if you don't then it wouldn't be. My friend's dad has a boat and he cut his finger off. He was trying to cut a rope and he slipped and he cut his finger. I was going out on a fish with my aunties and uncles and we caught a fish and it was a red fish and it had four fins.

You should watch the news and the weather forecast. A good friend of mine's dad got lost at sea. He was fishing. He was found past Saltese Island. The funeral was here across the road. The funeral was huge. There were loads of people standing outside the church because there wasn't enough room inside.

My uncle is a fisherman. He has a little boat and he has one person or he goes out on his own. It's more dangerous to go out on your own.

Callum

"It was a nice day but it went really bad."

W hen I was a baby we were in a boat and it tipped over. My mammy and my sister told me about it. They were trying to catch fish.

Aoife O'Shea

M y friend's dad is a diver. He looks for things for museums. You need the right equipment. You have to go down bit by bit. This fellow was out and his dad got killed. The boat tipped over. It was a nice day but it went really bad. They were out for a really long time.

Jenny

T hey have nets on the boats. If you're holding on to them and you put your hand in the wrong place you could fall off the side.

Megan

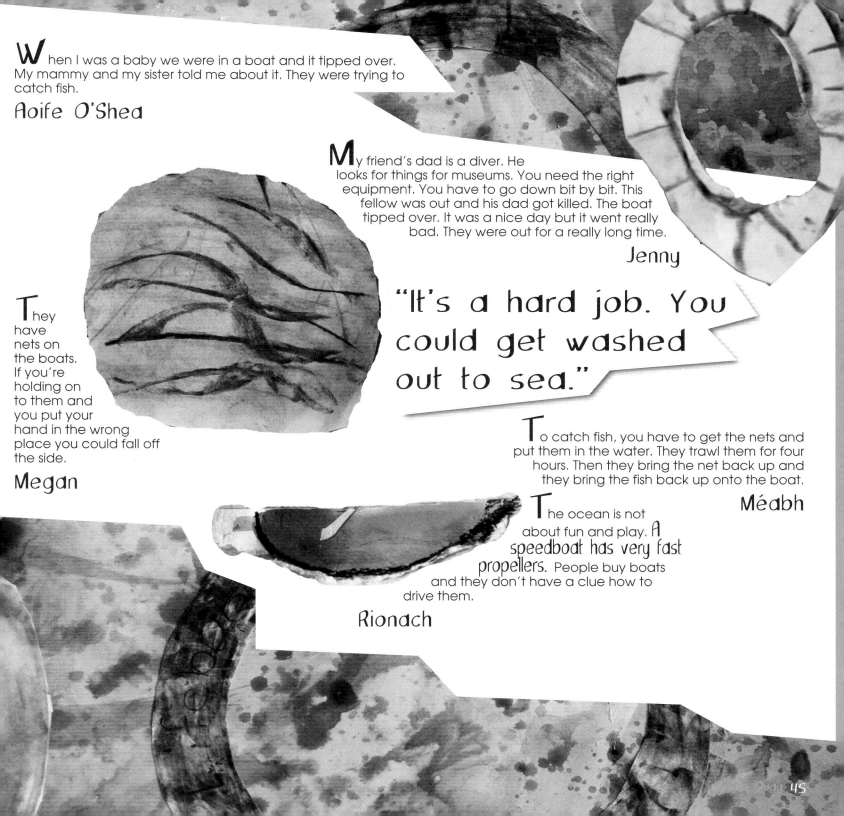

"It's a hard job. You could get washed out to sea."

T o catch fish, you have to get the nets and put them in the water. They trawl them for four hours. Then they bring the net back up and they bring the fish back up onto the boat.

Méabh

T he ocean is not about fun and play. A speedboat has very fast propellers. People buy boats and they don't have a clue how to drive them.

Rionach

I went on my friend's dad's boat. It was a speedboat. We went fishing.

Patrick

I was sitting on the wall and my dad fell in (when we were fishing). There was a rope hanging off the wall and he climbed back up.

Paddy

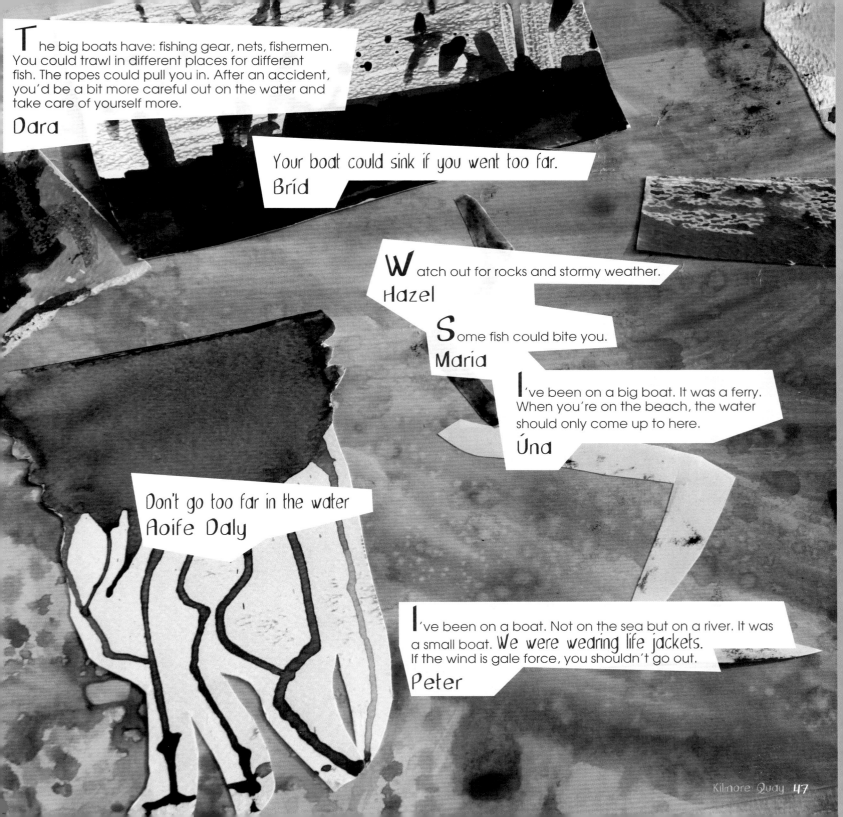

The big boats have: fishing gear, nets, fishermen. You could trawl in different places for different fish. The ropes could pull you in. After an accident, you'd be a bit more careful out on the water and take care of yourself more.

Dara

Your boat could sink if you went too far.

Bríd

Watch out for rocks and stormy weather.

Hazel

Some fish could bite you.

Maria

I've been on a big boat. It was a ferry. When you're on the beach, the water should only come up to here.

Úna

Don't go too far in the water

Aoife Daly

I've been on a boat. Not on the sea but on a river. It was a small boat. We were wearing life jackets. If the wind is gale force, you shouldn't go out.

Peter

Participants

Killybegs – Northwest

Donegal Education Centre

Abi Hutchinson, 2nd Class
Killaghtee NS, Dunkineely, Co. Donegal

Jane Curley, 3rd Class
Ballyraine NS, Letterkenny, Co. Donegal

Niamh McGeoghegan, 6th Class
St Mary's NS, Malin Head, Co. Donegal

Tomás Carr, Junior Infants
St Francis's NS, Barnesmore, Co. Donegal

Children from fishing community

Carla Morrow, 2nd Class
Killaghtee NS, Dunkineely, Co. Donegal

Shaun Boyle, 3rd Class
Fintra NS, Killybegs, Co. Donegal

Penelope Statham, 4th Class
Fintra NS, Killybegs, Co. Donegal

Andrea Furey, 6th Class
Bruckless NS, Co. Donegal

Orla Carbery, 6th Class
Bruckless NS, Co. Donegal

Aoife Cassidy, Junior Infants
St. Francis NS, Barnesmore, Co. Donegal

Laoise McBride, Junior Infants
St. Francis NS, Barnesmore, Co. Donegal

Sligo Education Centre

Ciara Lindsay, 5th Class
Ransboro NS, Sligo

Rimsha Khan, 3rd Class
Carbury NS, The Mall, Sligo

Alina Moran, 2nd Class
St Joseph's NS, Cullens, Co. Sligo

Trudie Moran, Senior Infants
St Joseph's NS, Cullens, Co. Sligo

Mayo Education Centre

Jennifer Blakeney, 1st Class
St Oliver Plunkett NS, Ballina, Co. Mayo

Shane Mullarkey, 4th Class
Scoil Croí Ró Naofa, Erris, Co. Mayo

Cian Mangan, Senior Infants
Cloghans Hill NS, Tuam, Co. Galway

Tara Doocey, 5th Class
Geesala NS, Ballina, Co. Mayo

Howth – East/ Northeast

Blackrock Education Centre

Christian Flood, 1st Class
St. Joseph's B.N.S, Terenure, Dublin 6

Jenna Rose Smyth, 5th Class
St. Joseph's National School, Glenealy, Co. Wicklow

Lily Glover, 3rd Class
Nun's Cross NS, Ashford, Co. Wicklow

Daniel Shea, Junior Infants
St. Patrick's NS, Curtlestown, Enniskerry, Co. Wicklow

Kildare Education Centre

Poppy Farrell, 2nd Class
Lacken NS, Lacken, Co. Kildare

Neena Pope, 3rd Class
Lacken NS, Lacken, Co. Kildare

Uchechi Uqwuegbulem, 6th Class
Scoil na Naomh Uilig, Newbridge, Co. Kildare

Christine Worrell, 4th Class
St John's NS, Monasterevan, Co. Kildare

Monaghan Education Centre

Dearbhla Ní Fhaircheallaigh, 4th Class
Scoil Roís, Carrickmacross, Co. Monaghan

Gabija Jankaitis, 1st Class
Bunscoil Lughaidh Naofa, Carrickmacross, Co. Monaghan

Calum Sherry, Senior Infants
St Louis Infant School, Monaghan Town, Co. Monaghan

David Kerley, 6th Class
Lisdonnan NS, Carrickmacross, Co. Monaghan

Navan Education Centre

Jack McMahon, 2nd Class
Scoil Mhuire na nGael, Bay Estate, Dundalk, Co. Louth

Alicia Burke, 3rd Class
Callystown NS, Clogherhead, Co. Louth

Orlaith Best, Senior Infants
St Ann's NS, Tierworker, Kells, Co. Meath

Ciaran O'Toole, 5th Class
Rathmore NS, Athboy, Co. Meath

Dublin West Education Centre

Ciara Moonman, Junior Infants
Castleknock Educate Together, Dublin 15

Anna Courtney, 6th Class
St Brigid's NS, Castleknock, Dublin 15

Lucy Meade, 2nd Class
Divine Word NS, Rathfarnham, Dublin 16

Claire Vance, 4th Class
St Martin's NS, Brittas, Co. Dublin

Drumcondra Education Centre

Ava Liddy, 4th Class
St Columba's NS, Glasnevin, Dublin 9

Seán Molony, 6th Class
St Patrick's BNS, Drumcondra, Dublin 9

Tom O'Neill, 2nd Class
St Patrick's BNS, Drumcondra, Dublin 9

Eva Vidal, Junior Infants
St Vincent De Paul Infant School, Marino, Dublin 9

Kilmore Quay – Southeast

Kilkenny Education Centre

Jack Power, 4th Class
Kilkenny School Project, Waterford Rd, Kilkenny

Andrew Donohue, 1st Class
Saplings School, Craiguecullen, Co. Carlow

Bríd Ryan, Junior Infants
Scoil Íosagáin, Thurles, Co. Tipperary

Rionach Maher, 5th Class
Scoil Ruadháin, Tulloran, Co. Kilkenny

Waterford Education Centre

Paddy McCarthy, Senior Infants
Carriglea NS, Ballyduff, Co. Waterford

Megan Roche, 5th Class
Rathgormack NS, Carrick-on-Suir, Co. Waterford

Peter Walsh, 5th Class
Rathgormack NS, Carrick-on-Suir, Co. Waterford

Jenny NicBhloscaigh, 4th Class
Scoil Gharbháin, Dungarvan, Co. Waterford

Laois Education Centre

Maeve Gallagher, 3rd Class
Arles NS, Ballickmoyler, Co. Laois

Aoife Daly, Junior Infants
Mountmellick NS, Mountmellick, Co. Laois

Aoife O'Shea, 2nd Class
Arles NS, Ballickmoyler, Co. Laois

Alyson Shaw, 6th Class
Maryborough NS, Portlaoise, Co. Laois

Wexford Education Centre

Dara Murray, 4th Class
St Canices NS, New Ross, Co. Wexford

Úna O'Dwyer, Senior Infants
Danescastle NS, Carrig-on-Bannow, Co. Wexford